Grade 5

The Syllabus of Examinations should be read for details of requirements, especially those for scales, aural tests and sight-reading. Attention should be paid to the Special Notices on the front inside cover, where warning is given of changes.

The syllabus is obtainable from music dealers or from The Associated Board of the Royal Schools of Music, 14 Bedford Square, London WC1B 3JG (please send stamped addressed envelope measuring about 9×6 ins.).

In overseas centres, information may be obtained from the Local Representative or Resident Secretary.

Requirements

SCALES AND ARPEGGIOS (from memory)

Scales
(i) in similar motion, hands together one octave apart, and each hand separately, in *all* major and minor keys (melodic *or* harmonic minor at candidate's choice) (all three octaves)
(ii) in contrary motion, both hands beginning and ending on the key-note (unison), in the keys specified in one of the following groups chosen by the candidate:
Group 1: A, F, Db majors and harmonic minors
Group 2: D, F♯, Bb majors and harmonic minors
(two octaves)

Chromatic Scales
(i) in similar motion, hands together one octave apart, and each hand separately, beginning on any note named by the examiner (three octaves)
(ii) in contrary motion, both hands beginning and ending on the same note (unison), beginning on D and Ab (two octaves)

Arpeggios
the major and minor common chords of *all* keys, in root position only, in similar motion, hands together one octave apart, and each hand separately (two octaves)

PLAYING AT SIGHT (see current syllabus)

AURAL TESTS (see current syllabus)

THREE PIECES

Candidates must prepare Nos.1 & 2 from the *same* list, A *or* B, but may choose No.3 from *either* list *or* one of the further alternatives listed below:

J. F. F. Burgmüller L'Hirondelle, Op.100 No.24
Haberbier Prelude in E minor
These are included in More Romantic Pieces for Piano, Book III, *published by the Associated Board*

Editor for the Associated Board: **Lionel Salter**

A:1
INVENTION in D minor

J.S. BACH, BWV 775

Source: autograph fair copy, Staatsbibliothek Preussischer Kulturbesitz, Berlin 1723. Phrasing, dynamics and ornaments in bars 17, 48 and 51 are editorial.   L.S.

A:2
SONATA in D
Second movement

Edited by
Howard Ferguson

CLEMENTI, Op.25 No.6

Un poco andante [♩ = c.84]

Source: the sixth of *Six Sonatas for the piano-forte*, Op.25 (J. Dale, London [1791]). The initial dynamic, the internal tempo indications, and the slurs in bars 7, 9, 11, 45, 47 & 49 are editorial.

AB 2353

A:3

CHA-CHA-CHA

from 'Melodie en Rhythme'

GERARD HENGEVELD

AB 2353

B:1
SONATA in A

[Andante, ♩ = c.116]

SCARLATTI, Kp.453

No autographs exist of Scarlatti's 550+ sonatas, but contemporary collections made by copyists are housed in Venice, Parma and Münster: there are small textual differences between them. The source adopted here is the last-named (No.52 in Volume 2 of the collection in the Universitäts-Bibliothek). Virtually all the slurs and the articulations in the present copy are editorial, as are the grace notes in bars 13, 45 & 47. Note that *all* grace notes should be played on the beat, not before it. Dynamics are left to the player's discretion.   L.S.

B:2
SONATA No.4 in F
First movement

Edited by
Timothy Roberts

STEPHEN STORACE

Source: *Six Easy and Progressive Sonatas for the Piano Forte or Harpsichord Compos'd for the Improvement of Juvenile Performers* (Longman & Broderip, London 1790). All dynamics and marks of articulation are editorial.

B:3
SCHERZO PASTORALE
from 'Reihe kleiner Klavierstücke'

HENK BADINGS

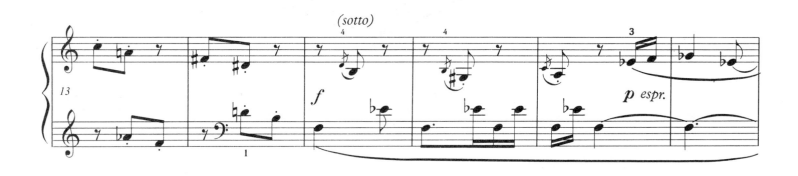

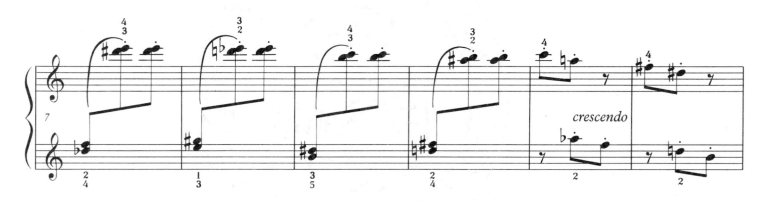